STRATEGIES
for better
MENTAL HEALTH

STRATEGIES for MOTIVATION
Learning ways to get unstuck!

Reproducible
Worksheets
for Teens
and Adults

D1225641

Nancy Day, OT Reg. (Ont.)

Illustrated by Amy L. Brodsky, LISW

STRATEGIES for MOTIVATION
Learning ways to get unstuck!

Library of Congress Catalog Card Number 2004108364

ISBN10: 1-893277-32-1
ISBN 13: 978-1-893277-32-8

WELLNESS REPRODUCTIONS & PUBLISHING

A Brand of The Guidance Group
1-800-669-9208
www.guidance-group.com

Dedication

This book is dedicated to those who experience mental illness.

⌐⌐⌐

Acknowledgements

The many hospital patients I have worked with over the years, have helped me write this book, albeit indirectly, by way of their questions, their stories, their difficulties and their triumphs. It is to them I give my sincerest thanks. I am also indebted to the fantastic team of clinicians at Markham Stouffville Hospital who cheerfully tolerate my need to try new ideas and just see what happens. Last, but not least, I am very, very thankful for the support of Estelle Leutenberg and Kathy Khalsa, at Wellness Reproductions & Publishing, who kindly gave me the opportunity to write this book and patiently helped me with every step along the way.

ᕬ Foreword ᕬ

INTRODUCTION
In the field of mental health, the issue of motivation is a significant one. Individuals experiencing mental illness invariably have difficulty with low motivation, poor energy levels and diminished hope for the future. This lack of motivation creates a challenge for mental health clinicians who are trying to help their clients make psychosocial, self-directed changes and achieve personal growth. When motivation is low, clients' commitment and ability to work toward therapeutic goals may be limited. There is often a need for therapists to focus on the issue of motivation and to help clients find practical solutions to get moving again.

USE OF WORKSHEETS
This is a collection of reproducible worksheets with facilitator's instructions for each worksheet. The facilitator's instructions provide a suggested format for using the worksheets, but can be changed and adapted to suit varying situations and settings. Although the worksheets are primarily designed for use with groups, they can be effectively used in individual counseling as well.

The book is laid out in a reasonably logical manner ranging from introductory, explanatory information on the topic of motivation to exercises for extremely challenging days. The worksheets, however, can be presented in any order, based on your particular clients and your day-to-day assessment about the needs of your group. Feel free to pick and choose, and to combine worksheets in any manner that works for you.

CHAPTER HEADINGS
Material is organized into five chapters, as follows. Chapter 1, ABOUT MOTIVATION provides some general and introductory information about the topic of motivation. Next, in BEING RESPONSIBLE FOR MY MOTIVATION, the worksheets deal with issues of taking ownership for the work involved in improving one's motivation. Chapter 3, called DIGGING DEEP FROM WITHIN, provides additional ideas involving participants reaching inside themselves for extra strength and wisdom. SMALL STEPS FOR DIFFICULT TIMES is included in the book as Chapter 4 to acknowledge the fact that recovery from mental illness can be very difficult and that some special strategies are warranted. Finally, Chapter 5, REACHING OUT / GETTING OUT focuses on strategies involved in getting out into the world with other people and for new experiences.

Using This Workbook

FACILITATING DISCUSSION

This book is not designed to provide basic information about group facilitation and leadership techniques. Suffice to say, an effective facilitator ensures an atmosphere where group members feel safe, respected and that their opinion counts. In the facilitator's instructions I provide suggestions about introducing discussion, drawing out concepts, asking pertinent questions, etc. — but use your own experience to initiate and manage discussion. Some of the techniques I frequently use are elaborated on more, as follows:

Warm-ups: Warm-ups are quick mini-exercises which are used at the beginning of a session to bring participants together as a group entity, establish a therapeutic climate and introduce concepts. Most of the facilitator's instructions suggest a way of "warming up" the group.

Flipcharts: Flipcharts or whiteboards are a vital piece of equipment in group work. They provide a visual aid in presenting information, brainstorming, asking pertinent questions, recording group members' ideas and a host of other purposes. Keep plenty of bright colored markers on hand, preferably non-toxic. Stimulate a sense of ownership in the group by involving participants in taking a turn at recording ideas on the flipchart.

Subdividing: This technique provides variation, physical movement, opportunity for shyer members to speak up, and reinforcement that participants have valuable wisdom of their own to share. Participants also get a break from listening to a facilitator. Vary the sizes of the subgroups from time to time, based on the requirements of the exercise. For some discussions pairs work well, while at other times a subgroup of four is more effective. Group members often find it difficult to form their own subgroups and might prefer being assigned by the facilitator. There are many creative ways for placing participants in their respective subgroups, besides the usual numbering off-try things like the color of shoes participants are wearing or the season in which participants are born. Aim to return to the large group before ending a session, even if it is only for a few minutes to hear any last comments or questions, and to provide for some closure.

Brainstorming: In the worksheets, a very loose definition of brainstorming is used — a means of gathering a lot of ideas. Establish a nonjudgmental climate for gathering participants' ideas in order to encourage them to share their own experiences and thoughts. Brainstorming can take place in the large group, small subgroups, pairs or individually. Recording can take place on the flipchart, worksheets or spare paper.

Reading Aloud: This technique is used in the book often. It is an effective way to present written material because it appeals to both visual and auditory intake of information. Ask for a volunteer to read — group members are usually quite agreeable about taking a turn. It is an opportunity for them to be involved. For some it is a big step to volunteer to read. Respect that it might be too difficult for some members to partake, for various reasons (literacy level, performance anxiety, etc.) and therefore it needs to be okay to decline. Always allow for some discussion, comments, questions and reactions to material read aloud.

Sharing: Groups seem to be most successful with sharing from group members. Participants all need to be offered an equal chance for "air-time." Quieter members need to be given ample opportunity to speak up, while overly-talkative members are appropriately curtailed. In mental health settings it is often prudent to have a rule of optional "passing" — that means it's okay and acceptable to say "pass." The sharing of personal information should remain the decision of the individual.

Round Robin: This technique is known by several names and provides a highly structured method of hearing from each participant. It involves posing a question to the group and then hearing each participant's response in an organized fashion by starting with one individual and simply continuing around the circle. It is time-effective, nicely manages overly-talkative individuals and provides a safe space in the discussion for more reticent and quieter members.

Homework: This can be a tricky area. Homework is an effective way to help participants apply what they are learning, but people sometimes associate it with unpleasant experiences from their school days. The term "homework" can even sound offensive to some adults. Try calling it something else — "home practice" or "ongoing implementation" — whatever works. You might try including participants in finding a name they like. No matter what it is called, it will be helpful for follow-through, if participants are helped to understand the benefits and purpose of homework.

One last word . . . enjoy yourself as you bring new ideas from this book to your group-work. Adapt, expand and improve on what is offered here, and then, share your successes with others. Good luck!

Table of Contents — sorted by topics

(over for table of contents sorted by Worksheet)

Table of Contents — sorted by worksheets

WORKSHEET	TOPIC	PAGE

ABOUT MOTIVATION

general introductory information

Motivation: What's That?

Motivation is an inner force that stirs a person to take certain action.
It is a very human quality, an aspect of being human that we are born with.
Babies are biologically hard-wired to grow, to learn, to move, to be curious and
to want things. There are many theories about motivation, which try to explain
where it comes from and how it works. Like many matters of the human mind,
the issues of motivation are complex and not completely clear. And to
make things more complicated . . . all people are unique.

A healthy level of motivation seems to be based on factors such as:
- experiencing success in one's efforts
- believing in oneself
- feeling a sense of control over one's surroundings
- knowing what is important to you
- having a desire to learn and grow
- caring about how others see you

Unfortunately people can lose their motivation. Why?
There are different reasons why this might happen, some of which include:
- too many negative or painful experiences
- loss of hope
- feeling helpless to change things or control one's environment
- poor self esteem or an absence of faith in oneself
- illnesses such as depression, schizophrenia or substance abuse problems
  (where poor motivation is a very real and genuine symptom)

HERE'S THE GOOD NEWS!

The good news is that motivation can be improved and / or re-learned —
gradually, slowly, with support, and with some effort. Getting your motivation
back means learning new strategies to encourage yourself, learning how to
utilize other peoples' support, beginning to build new positive experiences,
changing your negative self-talk about yourself and your efforts, learning
to be your own cheerleading section and starting to set reasonable and
realistic goals for yourself and your future. Interested? Sign up right here:

I pledge to work on improving my motivation. And signing this is the first step!

_____
(signature)

Facilitator's Instructions for
MOTIVATION: WHAT'S THAT?

When:	Use this worksheet to introduce the topic of motivation and to provide some initial explanatory information.

Why:	Motivation can be a difficult concept. It is an abstract idea, and not clearly understood even by experts in the field. Group participants struggling with low motivation need some help in understanding some basic principles but probably do not need to be overwhelmed by lengthy and detailed textbook explanations or theories on the subject.

What:

1. Write the word motivation on the flipchart. Ask participants to share the first thought that comes to mind when they see this word. Flipchart their responses. Use their responses to facilitate some discussion about the challenges they experience with their motivation.

2. Distribute the worksheet. Read it aloud or have a participant volunteer to read aloud.

3. Allow for discussion of participants' thoughts and ideas about the information on the worksheet. Facilitate discussion using a few of the following questions:

    • How does it feel to be poorly motivated?

    • How is it affecting your daily living?

    • How have you been attempting to cope with your lack of motivation?

    • How do you feel about signing your name to the bottom of the page?

    • Why might the act of signing the page be an important step?

4. This may be a good opportunity to provide any information participants will need regarding what to expect in upcoming groups, any expectations you have for their participation, etc.

5. Conclude by having participants show their signatures to those sitting next to them. At this point allow for anyone not comfortable in signing the page to leave it blank — as it might be a very difficult step for some.

HOW'S YOUR MOTIVATION?

Date: _____

How would you rate your level of motivation during the past week?
Please circle a number which best describes it:

1	2	3	4	5
poor	fair	moderate	good	excellent

What tasks are you able to accomplish?

_____

_____

_____

_____

_____

_____

What tasks are you finding difficult to accomplish?

_____

_____

_____

_____

_____

_____

Facilitator's Instructions for
HOW'S YOUR MOTIVATION?

When: Use this worksheet to have participants rate their level of motivation. This worksheet can be combined with any of the other worksheets/exercises in the book, or used alone.

Why: Completing a rating scale indicating their current level of motivation can provide a means for participants to track their progress as they begin to learn and practice motivational strategies. The worksheet asks participants to rate the motivation over the past week versus just one day, in order to help them see some general patterns rather than the minor fluctuations that occur from day to day.

What:
1. Distribute worksheets and ask participants to complete.

2. Allow for some sharing (optional).

3. Encourage participants to record their rating scales for easy reference, so they can track patterns and progress.

4. Repeat from time to time.

~ Let's De-bunk ~
MYTHS ABOUT MOTIVATION

1. Motivation can only come from within.
   DEBUNK:
   _____

2. To get motivated wait until you feel like doing something.
   DEBUNK:
   _____

3. In order to get the day off to a good start, stay in bed until you feel completely wide-awake.
   DEBUNK:
   _____

4. Social plans should not be made unless you feel 100% motivated to go and certain you can follow through.
   DEBUNK:
   _____

5. Successful participation in social events requires a lot of confidence and social graces. And, if it didn't feel like fun, it wasn't worth going.
   DEBUNK:
   _____

6. Strive for perfection and don't settle for anything less.
   DEBUNK:
   _____

7. If you start to feel shaky, scared or anxious about trying something new, put it off until you feel more motivated.
   DEBUNK:
   _____

8. Resting or napping is the best way to restore energy and oomph.
   DEBUNK:
   _____

Facilitator's Instructions for
LET'S DE-BUNK...MYTHS ABOUT MOTIVATION

When:

Use this worksheet as a way of providing basic information about issues relating to motivation. It is particularly effective when your clients have some faulty beliefs about how to get motivated.

Why:

People who have been unmotivated over a long period of time, may have developed some unrealistic, and even sabotaging, ways of viewing the issue of getting themselves moving. One way to address this is to talk about these faulty beliefs as "myths" and to enlist the group in a "debunking" exercise. Use MYTHS DE-BUNKED, page 9, for facts on myths.

What:

1. Explain that this exercise will help participants gain a better understanding about how motivation works.

2. Distribute handouts. Allow several minutes for participants to read over the page of myths. Or alternatively, ask for a volunteer to read the page aloud.

3. Divide into subgroups of 3 or 4, and provide instructions for them to "debunk" each myth. If there are time constraints, assign only a few myths to each subgroup. Allow sufficient time for this small group discussion.

4. Return to the large group and have each small group report back on their findings and the process of "debunking." Allow for discussion of differing viewpoints.

5. Ask each participant to identify and share the most important thing they learned from the "debunking."

MYTHS De-bunked

⊚ **MOTIVATION CAN ONLY COME FROM WITHIN.**

Motivation comes to us in different ways, both from within and without. To a great extent our inner beliefs create our level of motivation. But outside factors can provide motivation as well - other people, deadlines, money, etc. We must, however, be open to allowing these outside incentives to stimulate and move us.

⊚ **TO GET MOTIVATED, WAIT UNTIL YOU FEEL LIKE DOING SOMETHING.**

You might have to wait forever if you believe this. We can still do things when we do not feel like it. Do what you know is right, not what you feel. And remember, feeling interested in things often grows during activity rather than before we start — so if you do not feel motivated beforehand — persevere anyways! Momentum will kick in.

⊚ **IN ORDER TO GET THE DAY OFF TO A GOOD START, STAY IN BED UNTIL YOU FEEL COMPLETELY WIDE - AWAKE.**

You will probably sleep the day away if you try this. Realistically, very few people wake up in the morning feeling wide awake. Most of us also need a shower, some movement, a coffee, and/or something to focus on. Try rising at the same time each day.

⊚ **SOCIAL PLANS SHOULD NOT BE MADE UNLESS YOU FEEL 100% MOTIVATED TO GO AND CERTAIN YOU CAN FOLLOW THROUGH.**

Don't wait for this to happen or you may never make social plans. Operate from the assumption you will enjoy yourself and benefit from attending, but acknowledge that, at times, a change of plans may be necessary.

⊚ **SUCCESSFUL PARTICIPATION IN SOCIAL EVENTS REQUIRES A LOT OF CONFIDENCE AND SOCIAL GRACES, AND, IF IT DIDN'T FEEL LIKE FUN, IT WASN'T WORTH GOING.**

This attitude just creates avoidance of social gatherings. And it is not realistic. Social skills and social confidence need time to develop gradually, and with a lot of practice. And when it doesn't feel like fun, that's okay. Be patient and view it as an opportunity to learn.

⊚ **STRIVE FOR PERFECTION AND DON'T SETTLE FOR ANYTHING LESS.**

What better way to kill motivation! It is unrealistic and defeating to set perfectionist standards for yourself. No one is perfect — accept it.

⊚ **IF YOU START TO FEEL SHAKY, SCARED OR ANXIOUS ABOUT TRYING SOMETHING NEW, PUT IT OFF UNTIL YOU FEEL MORE MOTIVATED.**

Do not let fear stop you! It's okay to feel anxious or shaky. In fact, it is quite normal. Continue anyways. The anxiety will subside.

⊚ **RESTING OR NAPPING IS THE BEST WAY TO RESTORE ENERGY AND OOMPH.**

Resting sometimes helps. But often you still feel like doing nothing. Try renewing yourself with activity - the more physical the better.

Facilitator's Instructions for
MYTHS DE-BUNKED

When:

This worksheet can be used in combination with the debunking worksheet, entitled LET'S DEBUNK — MYTHS ABOUT MOTIVATION (see page 7) or on its own.

Why:

After using the LET'S DEBUNK — MYTHS ABOUT MOTIVATION worksheet, it may be apparent that the debunking was a difficult task for some individuals. They may have found it hard to challenge long-held beliefs about getting moving, trying new activities, etc. For these individuals or groups it may be helpful to also provide this printed fact sheet.

What:

1. Distribute this worksheet at the conclusion of the LET'S DEBUNK — MYTHS ABOUT MOTIVATION exercise.

2. Ask for a participant to volunteer to read the page aloud for the group.

3. Discuss any points or issues that have not been covered by the previous discussion.

Or, for use as a stand-alone worksheet, try this:

1. Introduce the concept of myths and the need to examine long-held beliefs for their relevance and truth. To stimulate some thought about this concept, ask participants to share a belief they remember having as a young child, that in retrospect is now absurd and funny, e.g., I used to think that cats were the girls and dogs were the boys.

2. Distribute the worksheet.

3. Read and discuss each myth, one at a time. For each myth, facilitate some group discussion using the following questions:

   - Have you believed this myth?

   - How has your belief in this myth effected your day-to-day functioning?

   - How ready are you to accept the facts relating to this myth, as presented on the worksheet?

MY MOTIVATION *feels like . . .*

WHICH PHRASE BEST DESCRIBES YOUR MOTIVATION?

The little engine that could

A slippery slope

Swimming among sharks

Camping in the rain

Snowboarding without the board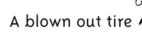

A bucket with a hole in it

A blossoming tree

Awakening to a sunny day

Stuck in quick sand

An eagle soaring

Bacon sizzling in the frying pan

Learning to walk again

A blown out tire

A spark about to catch fire

A piece of cake

Driving under the speed limit

Or, write your own _____

11

Facilitator's Instructions for
MY MOTIVATION FEELS LIKE . . .

When:

This worksheet might be used in several ways:
- To take a quick barometer of participant's motivation level to lead into another worksheet. (Activity A. below)
- On its own to stimulate a more in-depth discussion of the images and feelings associated with the issue of motivation. (Activity B. below)

Why:

Feelings need to be acknowledged and expressed in order for individuals to move on or resolve issues. This worksheet provides a means of exploring how participants feel — and to help them to be heard by others.

What:

A.

1. To take a quick reading of participants' level of motivation, distribute the worksheet and instruct participants to circle the phrase best describing their motivation.
2. Allow for sharing and comments.
3. Move on to a second worksheet of your choice.

B.

1. Explain that this session will provide an opportunity for participants to reflect on, and share, their inner experience of motivation (or lack of).
2. Distribute the worksheet and have participants circle the phrase best describing their motivation.
3. Next have them use the blank space at the bottom of the page to write down three additional "feeling" words to describe their inner experience. Some participants might need coaching to understand what "feeling" words are — take a few minutes to do this.
4. Pair group members and allow time for them to share what they wrote on their worksheets.
5. Return to the large group. Ask if there are any participants who described their motivation in positive words such as "awakening to a sunny day." Ask those group members to share how they got there or to provide some words of encouragement to other participants whose experience with motivation feels more negative and difficult.
6. Conclude by reminding group members that feelings are neither right nor wrong, good nor bad - they just are - and they pass as we allow ourselves to experience, acknowledge and express them.

The Downward Spiral of Poor Motivation

Opportunity for action

Negative thoughts about the opportunity

Decision made to not take part

Lack of action

More negative thinking and motivation worsens

Further withdrawal and inactivity

Facilitator's Instructions for
THE DOWNWARD SPIRAL OF POOR MOTIVATION

When: Use this worksheet to shed light on the vicious cycle that may get set in motion when there is a loss of motivation due to illness or other devastating circumstance.

Why: Loss of motivation may begin as a symptom of an illness such as depression, schizophrenia or substance abuse problems. But, when low motivation persists despite improvement in illness, it may be hanging on for other reasons — it may simply have become a habit (particularly the habit of negative thinking) — or it may now be based on fear and/or loss of confidence resulting from long periods of inactivity and avoidance. There may also be a secondary gain from inactivity like pity or attention.

What:

1. Introduce the idea that loss of motivation can be viewed and understood as being part of a vicious cycle that an individual is not necessarily aware of.

2. Distribute the worksheets. Explain and elaborate on the steps shown on the Downward Spiral.

3. Facilitate discussion using the following questions. Do participants see themselves in this spiral? In what ways is the downward spiral evident in their lives? What kinds of tasks, activities or responsibilities do they avoid doing because of this phenomenon?

4. Now give them the good news: THE SPIRAL CAN BE BROKEN!

5. Sub-divide into small groups or partners. Ask them to develop and record some ideas on how to break out of the downward spiral.

6. Return to the large group to hear their ideas.

7. In round robin fashion, ask each participant for one change she or he will make based on today's activity.

MOTIVATION
RAISERS & WRECKERS

Ways to WRECK your motivation:

Ways to RAISE your motivation:

Facilitator's Instructions for
MOTIVATION RAISERS & WRECKERS

When:

Use this worksheet to help participants develop awareness of strategies that improve motivation as well as the traps that defeat motivation. This exercise works well to reinforce learning from previous sessions.

Why:

In this structured exercise individuals struggling with motivation have an opportunity to teach and learn from each other. Suggestions coming from those experiencing similar difficulties are often easier to accept than suggestions from a "professional," so provide a forum for participants to be the experts they truly are.

What:

1. Suggest that participants teach each other in this session what they have learned along the way. Remind them that they all have many good ideas on how to improve motivation as well as how to "wreck" it.

2. Form two sub-groups in the following way. Have participants choose to sit on either side of the room — one side for individuals who would be willing to share their own experiences and knowledge about how to *raise motivation*. On the other side, seat those who have learned, perhaps the hard way, how to *wreck motivation* and are willing to share that information with the group.

3. Distribute the worksheets and have each subgroup brainstorm and list their ideas on the worksheet.

4. Provide time for the subgroups to develop a presentation or role play illustrating one or several of their ideas. Encourage creativity.

5. Reconvene to the large group and have each subgroup present to the large group. Encourage feedback.

6. Conclude by asking participants how they enjoyed the experience of learning from one another. Ask what they will take away from the session to help with their motivation.

10 STRATEGIES FOR GETTING MOTIVATED

1. **MAKE A COMMITMENT:** Commit yourself by making a plan, writing it on the calendar and sharing your plan with another person.

2. **CALENDAR OR DAY BOOK:** Write tasks and activities down on a wall calendar or small day book. Carry your day book with you, and look at it frequently. Check things off when completed.

3. **THINK OF ALL THE RESOURCES AVAILABLE TO YOU:** Who and what might be able to help you to follow through with your plan or commitment? What creative ideas can you think of to get around obstacles? Ask for help if you need it.

4. **BE OPEN MINDED TO NEW IDEAS:** Recognize that trying to do things the same old way may not be working for you. Listen to how others are getting things done. Try the suggestions of others.

5. **VISUALIZE THE POSITIVE BENEFITS:** Think about all the positives you will get from following through with the task or activity. Imagine the sense of accomplishment you will feel later.

6. **ONE STEP AT A TIME:** Break activities down into manageable steps, to avoid feeling overwhelmed. It is easier to get started if you remind yourself it is okay to just do the first step.

7. **ACTION BEFORE INTEREST:** Remember that the feeling of being interested in an activity often sets in after starting the activity, not before. Get started on something no matter how you feel, and the interest will come. Try activities even if you initially feel tired, bored, nervous or uninterested.

8. **THE BUDDY SYSTEM:** It is often easier to get moving when you have the support of a friend with whom to face a challenge. Go to a new activity with a friend or supportive family member.

9. **KEEP YOUR EXPECTATIONS REALISTIC:** What are your expectations for yourself when trying something new? Keep them realistic. Do not aim for perfection. Expect to feel nervous. Expect to make mistakes. Expect it to feel difficult.

10. **DO THE FIVE TIMES TEST:** When joining a new activity, club or class do not make a decision about quitting until you have attended at least five times. It is not fair to judge the merits of something until you have given it a fair chance. That's five times!

Facilitator's Instructions for
10 STRATEGIES FOR GETTING MOTIVATED

When:

Use this list of ten strategies to either:
  a. provide new ideas, or to
  b. reinforce / summarize learning that has taken place in previous groups.

Why:

Depending on the needs of the group, this worksheet can be used in either way. A group may need to be provided with a list of new motivational strategies to discuss and then try putting into practice. Alternatively, a group may benefit from reviewing strategies previously discussed.

What:

1. Divide participants into pairs. Instruct the pairs to create a list of strategies for getting motivated, which they have either learned from past groups or ideas they have initiated on their own. Provide table space, flipchart paper and markers.

2. Have each pair present their flipcharted ideas back to the large group, encouraging comments and questions from the others.

3. Ask for a group member to volunteer to input the flipcharted ideas onto a home computer and print copies. These can be distributed to all group members at a later time.

4. Distribute the worksheet, explaining that the ten strategies listed are in addition to what has already been presented by participants. Read aloud, elaborating as necessary, and commenting on any overlap with ideas presented by the participants.

5. Conclude by having each person choose a new strategy he or she is willing to try in the next few days.

BEING RESPONSIBLE FOR MY MOTIVATION

looking at taking ownership for the work involved in improving motivation

Learning Log

Date:

Topic:

Something important I learned in this discussion:

I will put my learning into action by:

Facilitator's Instructions for
LEARNING LOG

When:

Use this worksheet as an adjunct to other worksheets, activities and / or discussions, to focus participants' attention on important learning points.

Why:

Participants, even with the best of intentions, can forget what they have heard in group discussions. For some individuals, concentration might be impaired. Sometimes there is a diminished ability to utilize a "classroom" environment. At times, group participants might feel overwhelmed by trying to remember everything they have heard in a session. This worksheet can help to focus, emphasize or reinforce important learning from group sessions, as well as to stress the importance of taking action and applying new learning.

What:

1. Leave between 5 – 10 minutes for this Learning Log at the end of a session.

2. Distribute the worksheet and have participants complete.

3. Depending on the needs of the group, as well as timing, try any of the following:

   a) Allow participants to keep their completed Logs private. Offer encouragement to make the most of their learning and to follow through with their "action."

   b) Provide an opportunity for participants to share what they wrote on their Logs.

   c) Have participants report back on the outcome of their actions at a later group session.

What MOTIVATES You?
survey

Different things motivate different people. Your motivation may be low right now, but by identifying what tends to motivate you, you may find some ways to move yourself forward. Have a look at the list below and check off items that apply to you. It is not a complete list, so add your own ideas.

- [ ] Doing my best
- [ ] Others depending on me
- [ ] Being complimented or encouraged by others
- [ ] Seeing the positive results of my actions
- [ ] Being around positive people
- [ ] Proving something to myself
- [ ] Proving something to others
- [ ] Feeling of accomplishment
- [ ] Last minute pressure
- [ ] Wanting independence
- [ ] Seeing my children happy
- [ ] Conflict

- [ ] Money
- [ ] Enjoying a sense of pride in my actions
- [ ] Having to meet a deadline
- [ ] Learning new things
- [ ] Enjoying the challenge
- [ ] To avoid the pressures caused by procrastination
- [ ] To avoid criticism from others
- [ ] To avoid feeling guilty
- [ ] Getting encouragement from others
- [ ] _____
- [ ] _____

Select one of your motivators that was checked from the list above:

_____

Now develop a plan for using this to enhance your low motivation. For instance, if "Getting encouragement from others" is one of your motivators, consider asking a friend or family member for this type of support in a particular area where you need a push.

See if you can make another plan for any of the other motivators that you checked.

Facilitator's Instructions for
WHAT MOTIVATES YOU?

| **When:** | Use this worksheet to help group members identify what motivates them. |

| **Why:** | Participants may need encouragement to explore what has motivated them in the past and to a certain extent continue to motivate them now. This worksheet helps to identify some personal motivators and to start to think about capitalizing on them now in their daily lives. |

What:

1. Introduce the idea that different things motivate different people, and what motivated us when we were younger, may not motivate us right now. It can be helpful to know what kinds of things work for us personally.

2. Distribute the worksheet and instruct participants to check-off motivators on the list that apply to themselves, adding any others they can think of.

3. Instruct participants to complete the rest of the worksheet. It may be necessary to provide an example first.

4. Once they have completed the worksheet, provide some time for sharing of their ideas, either in subgroups or the large group.

5. Conclude with encouragement to implement the ideas they have come up with.

Negative Thinking and Motivation

As human beings we all have a mind with which to think - and that is exactly what we do all day — we think. We are not necessarily aware of all our thoughts since much of our thinking is so automatic, so quick, so habitual we do not even notice it. Many people refer to this as "self-talk."

A lot of our self-talk is about, who else? Me, myself and I. It is important to understand that many of our thoughts are not facts, just simply our opinions, perceptions and attitudes. Some of our self-talk is realistic, some is distorted from reality. Some thoughts are kind, some are cruel, some are motivational, some are just plain discouraging, and even paralyzing!

So depending on the way you think about yourself, you can either motivate yourself, or do the opposite and get yourself stuck. The trick is to become aware of your manner of thinking — is it kind and encouraging or is it destructive, cruel and critical?

Before getting out of bed in the morning, what goes through your head?
I can't do it.
or
This feels hard, but I'll try. I've done it before.

On your way to group what goes through your head?
I'm too stupid to say anything in the group.
or
Everyone has ideas worth sharing, including me.
If I can't speak up today, I'll try again tomorrow.

The good news is that everyone has the power to change their thinking. Our brain is our own! Once you start to become aware of your negative thinking, you can start working on changing it to a style of thinking that is more helpful and motivating. With practice, patience, support and persistence, you can re-learn how to think.

RE-LEARN...RE-THINK...RE-STRUCTURE...RE-ENERGIZE

Facilitator's Instructions for
NEGATIVE THINKING AND MOTIVATION

When: Use this worksheet to provide instruction on cognitive concepts and to illustrate the impact of negative thinking on one's motivation.

Why: Learning to restructure negative and faulty cognitions is an exceptionally helpful skill for many individuals struggling with issues of low motivation. Participants may be familiar with this concept, or may have very little understanding about the role their inner dialogue plays in their inability to get moving and work toward goals.

What:

1. To introduce the topic ask participants to think back to the first thought they were aware of having on awakening this morning. Ask them to share what the thought was.

2. Introduce the idea that our first thoughts of the morning can have an impact on how the day unfolds. Ask for their responses to this possibility.

3. Ask for a show of hands — how many of them think we have any control over what we think about? Did anyone exercise control over their initial thoughts on awakening today? Get several examples.

4. Distribute the worksheet. Review with the participants, clarifying and elaborating as needed.

5. Ask the participants who woke up today with negative thoughts — if they can offer a suggestion on changing their first thought of today — to one that is more encouraging, positive and kinder.

WHAT DO I DO WITH GROUP INFORMATION?

WONDERFUL!

NOTES & WORKSHEETS

☐ Store in a binder or file folder.
☐ Occasionally re-read and review.
☐ Refer to on "bad days" for ideas to try.
☐ Keep a journal or notebook on what I'm learning.
☐ Other _____

PRACTICING & USING

☐ Practice strategies I'm learning about.
☐ Practice over and over again!
☐ Try strategies more than once, even if they don't work the first time.
☐ Develop a wide variety of strategies to use.
☐ Other _____

SHARING

☐ Discuss what I'm learning with a close friend or family member.
☐ Share my progress with those I trust.
☐ Respect the confidentiality of names and personal information shared by other group members.
☐ Emphasize the positive aspects of group when I share.
☐ Use assertiveness to respond to criticism about what I'm doing at group.
☐ Other _____

NOT SO GOOD!

NOTES & WORKSHEETS

☐ Leave worksheets lying around the group room, forgetting to take home.
☐ File under "G" (the garbage).
☐ Stash here and there around the house, collecting dust.
☐ Other _____

PRACTICING & USING

☐ Neglect to work on logs and other assigned homework.
☐ Ignore group suggestions and continue to do things pretty much the way I always have!
☐ Maybe try things once, that's enough.
☐ Rely on just one coping strategy and hope it always works.
☐ Other _____

SHARING

☐ Criticize and speak sarcastically about others from group.
☐ Reveal confidential information about group members.
☐ Decline to share what I'm learning with anyone.
☐ Dwell on the things I don't like about group.
☐ Other _____

Facilitator's Instructions for
WHAT DO I DO WITH GROUP INFORMATION?

When: Use this worksheet as a means of reinforcing the information participants are learning in group. In particular, the worksheet provides ideas about how to organize themselves with group material and learning.

Why: Sometimes group attendees, despite enjoying the group experience, neglect to take group ideas and suggestions home to apply to their real lives. Participants may require some coaching about how to apply and make the most of the group experience, i.e. a system for keeping and utilizing printed worksheets and notes, further discussion at home about what they are learning and how they are progressing, and practicing and applying to their own lives the life skills and strategies they are learning.

What:

1. As a quick warm-up ask participants to share one thing they have learned from their group experience, so far.

2. Facilitate dialogue about what participants are doing with ideas they hear about during group discussions. In particular, what are they doing with group material out in the real world?

3. Distribute the worksheet and introduce its use. Provide time for completion.

4. Divide participants in subgroups and allow time for sharing from their completed worksheets.

5. Return to the large group. Ask for comments on what they have identified for themselves about their use of group information. A round robin approach works nicely for this.

TELEVISION: Friend or Foe

WHICH TV WATCHING STYLE BEST DESCRIBES YOU?

"ADDICTED"	"MIDDLE GROUND"	"WHO NEEDS IT"
The TV is always on.	I watch TV most days.	I seldom watch TV.
TV watching fills up much of my time; there is nothing else to do anyways.	I enjoy watching TV in my spare time.	I take part in a variety of hobbies, interests and activities.
I have very few (or no) hobbies or interests.	I have some other hobbies and interests which I take part in.	I have one or two TV shows I enjoy and sometimes make a point of watching them.
I watch TV when I really should be doing housework or errands or other activities.	Occasionally I watch too much TV but try to avoid making this a habit.	Most television shows seem to be of poor quality and a complete waste of time.
I often get to bed quite late because I can't turn the TV off, and then I'm late for things in the morning.	I perform my responsibilities without letting TV interfere.	I would never let watching TV interfere with anything else I should be doing.
I feel deprived if I have to turn the TV off.	I take breaks between household chores and other responsibilities to watch a bit of TV.	Most of the time I'm too busy with my life to watch much TV.
I find it hard to find the energy and/or time to work toward any goals.	I enjoy TV in the evenings but turn it off at a reasonable hour so that I can get to bed.	It wouldn't bother me at all if the TV broke and I couldn't afford the repairs.
	I can usually work toward my goals without letting the TV interfere.	

See Facilitator's Instructions for
TELEVISION: FRIEND OR FOE
on page 32

TELEVISION: Friend or Foe
SELF REFLECTION

MY TELEVISION VIEWING STYLE IS BEST DESCRIBED AS:

ADDICTED   MIDDLE GROUND   WHO NEEDS IT!

1. Describe in your own words the role TV has in your life.

_____

_____

_____

_____

2. Describe how your TV watching habits effect your motivation.

_____

_____

_____

_____

3. What would (or could) improve in your life if you changed your TV watching habits?

_____

_____

_____

_____

Identify one step you will commit to making:

_____

SIGNATURE

Facilitator's Instructions for
TELEVISION: FRIEND OR FOE
AND
TELEVISION: FRIEND OR FOE — SELF REFLECTION

When:

Use this worksheet when you suspect poor TV watching habits may be having a negative impact on participants' abilities to work on their goals.

Why:

The issue of excessive TV viewing is often overlooked. Participants may have fallen into very destructive and sabotaging television habits, learned either as children or developed on their own as adults. People are often unaware of the extent to which they squander their time watching TV. They may not realize they use TV to avoid people or responsibilities. They may not see the impact it has on their motivation. And it may even have become an addiction for some. These two worksheets serve to shed some light on this issue.

What:

1. Generate some initial discussion by asking for a quick show of hands on the following questions:

    - How many of you watch TV?

    - How many of you have had family or friends tell you that you watch too much TV?

    - How many of you think TV is a problem for you? (Have them elaborate.)

2. Distribute the worksheet titled TELEVISION: FRIEND OR FOE, page 29, and instruct participants to read over and identify the style best reflecting their TV habits.

3. Now distribute the worksheet TELEVISION: FRIEND OR FOE — SELF REFLECTION, page 31, and have participants circle their television viewing style and then answer the first three questions.

4. Place participants in small subgroups for sharing.

5. Reconvene in the large group and ask for thoughts and comments.

6. Conclude by having willing participants complete the final box, committing themselves to a change.

FINDING MEANING IN THE BIGGER PICTURE

Every small task facing us is part of a bigger picture. Reminding yourself about the bigger picture can help you put things in perspective and help you see the real meaning behind your actions, the larger purpose, the reasons for putting forth so much effort into the smaller tasks of daily living.

Try drawing a line to connect the small task to the bigger picture.
There's no one correct answer, but various ways the lines can be drawn.

SMALL TASK	BIGGER PICTURE
Getting out of bed	Having a satisfying social life
Phoning about a volunteer job	Getting an education
Going for a walk	Establishing long-term mental health
Starting to say "no"	Finding a life partner
Joining a bowling club	Achieving the respect of family
Learning to use recipes	Earning an income
Doing a crossword puzzle	Having a healthy body weight
Initiating invitations	Becoming independent

Starting to see how smaller steps fit into the bigger picture is the first step.
Next, in a very conscious manner, you need to practice refocusing yourself
on what the bigger picture is for you.

TRY THIS:

Identify a small task you are finding difficult to complete:

What is the bigger picture for you?

Facilitator's Instructions for
FINDING MEANING IN THE BIGGER PICTURE

When: Use this worksheet to help group members frame the small, sometimes meaningless tasks of the day into a way that brings more awareness to the "bigger picture" to which they aspire.

Why: Individuals with low motivation may find themselves questioning the necessity of carrying through with seemingly small, but difficult, daily tasks and goals. Why bother? They may lose sight of their long-term goals. This worksheet shows them a way of gaining a larger perspective in order to focus on the real reasons for working hard on all these small steps.

What:

1. Introduce the concept by asking participants to share a small step they took yesterday or today. Following this, ask them to share why they took this step.

2. Distribute the worksheet and have the first paragraph read aloud by one of the group members. Ask for comments and reactions to the concept, and make a connection to the sharing in step 1.

3. Assign group members to pairs and instruct them to complete the next part of the worksheet connecting "small tasks" to the "bigger picture."

4. Discuss this process and their answers in large group format.

5. Have participants complete the box entitled "TRY THIS." Allow time for sharing. Facilitate discussion about their thoughts on the usefulness of this strategy for trying to get more motivated.

DIGGING DEEP FROM WITHIN

*strategies that pull strength
from within oneself*

To move

◌ **The Latin root of the word "motivation" means . . ."to move."** ◌

Reflect on the word "move." Read the following questions and without thinking too hard, write down some of the first things that come to mind.

What *moves* you in nature?

_____

_____

_____

If you could *move* to a new location (anywhere in the world) where would it be? Why?

_____

_____

_____

What is an important *move* you want to make? (physical, emotional, spiritual, emotional)

_____

_____

_____

What helps you to *move* yourself?

_____

_____

_____

Facilitator's Instructions for
TO MOVE

When:

Use this worksheet to get to know participants in a new group situation and/or when they do not know each other very well.

Why:

Participants may need time to acclimate to a group format. The first two questions on the worksheet are of fairly low-demand for new participants and tend to generate answers that are nonthreatening for sharing in a group setting. The final two questions require a bit more thought and self-reflection, and begin to explore the issue of motivation.

What:

1. Let participants know they will be doing some writing and a small amount of sharing. Reassure them that they are in control of what they choose to share.

2. Plan a light, get-to-know-you exercise to start things off. Here are two suggestions. Use one or both:

   a) Have participants share their name and one other thing they would be comfortable sharing with the group, such as their favorite ice cream or how they like their eggs cooked.

   b) With a marker, write the letters of the words TO MOVE down the left hand side of the flipchart. Ask participants to share a place they have traveled that starts with one of the letters. Flipchart their answers beside the corresponding letter. In a light manner, remark on how well-traveled the group is!

3. Distribute the worksheets and ask participants to complete. Plan to have soft music playing in the background.

4. Invite sharing of one of their answers (their choice). This can be done in pairs, small subgroups or in the large group — depending on your assessment of their comfort level.

5. Wrap up by providing some details about what they can expect at future groups.

the "JUST DO IT" approach

Often the JUST DO IT approach works!

It is especially helpful when the real problem is procrastination. Stress can build from knowing you really need to take care of something or should be working toward a goal or plan you have set for yourself. Eliminate the stress by just doing it.

Identify a goal, step or activity you would like to JUST DO:

_____

_____

I will JUST DO IT because
(list all the benefits you would receive if you just did it):

_____

_____

_____

_____

_____

_____

_____

_____

I will JUST DO IT.

_____
(signature)

Facilitator's Instructions for
THE "JUST DO IT" APPROACH

When: Use this worksheet to re-introduce this age old, tried-but-true strategy for getting things done. It can be especially effective for procrastinators because it helps them focus on the benefits of "just doing."

Why: Participants have probably tried to "just do it" many times— sometimes failing, sometimes succeeding. This worksheet gives the approach a catchy name and draws attention to the crux of the matter, i.e., concentrating on the pleasant and rewarding aftermath of one's potential efforts.

What:

1. Write the words "JUST DO IT" on the flipchart.

2. Ask for participants' impressions of this often heard saying.

3. In round robin fashion, ask participants to identify and share a goal or step with which they are finding it hard to proceed and probably need to "just do."

4. Ask for permission from one of the participants to use their identified goal or step. Write on flipchart. Now have the group brainstorm the possible benefits for this group member of "just doing it." Record their ideas on the flipchart.

5. Distribute the worksheet and provide time for completion.

6. Facilitate discussion on their findings. Ask for a show of hands on how many signed their name to the bottom of the page. Ask how it feels to have signed it / not signed it. Ask group members to share any specifics of their plan, e.g., when, how, with whom.

7. Have participants report back on their success at a later date.

RECYCLING PAST MOTIVATION
~ self reflection ~

1. Describe a time in your life when you felt very motivated.

_____

_____

_____

_____

2. What did you accomplish with that motivation?

_____

_____

_____

_____

3. Can you pinpoint why you felt so motivated at that time?
   Or, in other words, where did the motivation come from?

_____

_____

_____

_____

4. Since then, what has happened to that motivation?

_____

_____

_____

_____

5. Is there possibly a helpful learning point from that time in your life which could
   be applied now to help with your motivation? What is it?

_____

_____

_____

_____

Facilitator's Instructions for
RECYCLING PAST MOTIVATION — SELF REFLECTION

When:

Use this worksheet to help the group reflect back on their lives to a time when they were very motivated.

Why:

Participants may need to be shown and reminded that old learning and experiences can be drawn on for re-use, refinement and recycling. Everyone has felt motivated at some point in their lives. Some set of factors motivated them back then — and there may be a clue from that past experience that could be brought forward to the present time, and in some manner be put in place to help now.

What:

1. Introduce the topic in a fun, light-hearted way by asking participants how many follow the three "R's" (re-use, refinement, recycling) of conservation. Elicit a few examples.

2. Make a link between recycling for the purpose of conservation and recycling of personal experiences. Suggest that previous life lessons and experiences can be reclaimed, recycled, adapted, modified, refined and re-used. Allow for discussion of their thoughts on this concept.

3. Distribute worksheets and provide time for participants to complete. Soft background music can augment this self-reflective exercise.

4. Divide participants into subgroups of three or four for sharing of the completed worksheets.

5. Return to the large group and facilitate discussion about their responses to question #5, by asking the following questions:
   - Can they apply anything from their past experiences to their present lives?
   - How could that help with their motivation now?
   - Have they heard any strategies today from other participants which they could use for themselves to improve motivation? Which ones?

SELF-TALK and MOTIVATION

THOUGHTS THAT HINDER:

___ I'll look stupid.

___ Why bother?

___ It's hard.

___ It's too hard.

___ I don't know how.

___ Everyone will stare at me.

___ I'll fail.

___ I'm too tired.

___ There's no point in trying.

___ I'm too fat.

___ I'll make a mistake.

___ Not today.

___ I won't know what to do.

___ I didn't ask for this.

___ I don't feel like it.

___ Why me?

OTHERS: _____

_____

THOUGHTS THAT HELP:

I'll try.

Just take the first step.

I do have a brain in my head.

I don't have to be perfect.

I can figure it out.

I'll try again tomorrow.

No one will bother to stare at me.

Other people will be kind.

I'll do my best.

We're all in the same boat — just human.

I've succeeded before.

I can accomplish something, no matter how small.

I'm not stupid, just scared.

It's okay to make mistakes.

Feeling anxious is okay.

Most people would be scared too.

I can ask for help.

It's not the end of the world.

OTHERS: _____

_____

Facilitator's Instructions for
SELF-TALK AND MOTIVATION

| **When:** | Participants will find this worksheet useful after completing the worksheet titled NEGATIVE THINKING, page 25. |

| **Why:** | Learning to restructure negative and faulty cognitions is an exceptionally helpful skill for many individuals struggling with issues of low motivation. Gaining awareness into one's negative self-talk, as well as learning with what to replace it, are both major strategies for combating poor motivation. This worksheet offers examples of common nonmotivating self-talk, as well as examples of ways to shift thinking to thoughts, that are more encouraging and motivating. |

What:

1. Distribute the worksheet.

2. Review the list of "Thoughts That Hinder." Ask participants to place a check beside the thoughts they recognize in themselves that hinder their motivation. Encourage them to add any others to the list that they are aware of having.

3. Next, review the list of "Thoughts That Help." Facilitate discussion about these examples of positive self-talk. Do participants think the thoughts make sense? Do they ever think this way? What happens when they do? Add any others they suggest to the list.

4. Instruct participants to circle their favorite positive thought from the list. Encourage each person to identify a situation from the past several days when this circled thought would have come in handy. Encourage them to also identify an upcoming event in which they may find it useful to use this particular self-talk.

5. Conclude by having each participant say their favorite positive thought aloud in a manner that is assertive, forceful, yet kind.

Relentless Determination – I

In an article printed in *Schizophrenia Digest,* David Rottmayer
says that key to his successful recovery is a **RELENTLESS DETERMINATION**
to make the most of his life and to stay well.

What do the words **RELENTLESS DETERMINATION** mean to you?

_____

_____

_____

Do you have a relentless determination to make the most of your life and to stay well?
Answer this question by circling a number on the following rating scale:

1	2	3	4	5
none at all				relentlessly determined

Please explain:

_____

_____

Write about an accomplishment you have had due to a high level of determination:

Facilitator's Instructions for
RELENTLESS DETERMINATION — I

When:

This worksheet can be used to talk about and explore the following concepts: a. taking personal responsibility, b. pushing oneself when the going gets tough and c. never giving up.

Why:

The phrase "relentless determination" provides the group with a break from the term motivation, though essentially the same thing. Participants need to consider how much effort and determination they are willing to put forth. David Rottmayer, who has a severe and persistent mental illness, speaks well to this issue in an article outlining his story. Individuals with similar struggles and challenges in their lives can be tremendously inspired by his testimonial.

What:

1. Read aloud the following excerpts from the article entitled "Philosophy of Life Helps David Rottmayer" by David Rottmayer, published in Schizophrenia Digest, Winter 2003 edition, page 31:

   "... Rottmayer remembers vividly the terrifying ride to the psychiatrist in 1992, when he was in the throes of psychotic delusions. With his father driving, he cowered in the back seat of the car, convinced the Columbian drug lords had a sniper waiting for him along the way...

   ... Now 33, the Spokane, Washington resident owns a condominium and a car, is happily married and is studying to become a certified professional accountant...

   How has he coped so remarkably well? To Rottmayer, it's a combination of factors: the fact he received treatment promptly, never missing taking his medication, the support of friends and relatives, and the fact that his parents had high expectations for him — even after he developed the illness. Also key to his recovery, he says is a **relentless determination** to make the most of his life and to stay well."

2. Ask for general comments, thoughts and reactions to David's story.
3. Distribute the worksheets and provide time for participants to complete.
4. Sharing of their worksheets could take various forms:
   a) in pairs, small subgroups, or the large group
   b) sharing of only parts of the worksheet or the whole thing.
5. Conclude by asking participants to identify and share with the large group a number on the rating scale to signify the level of determination they would like to achieve. Have them record this on their worksheet so that they can refer to it later.

Relentless Determination — II

In an article printed in *Schizophrenia Digest,* David Rottmayer says that key to his successful recovery is a **RELENTLESS DETERMINATION** to make the most of his life and to stay well.

If you were to make the most of your life what kinds of things would you want to accomplish? List three if you can:

1._____

2._____

3._____

Choose one that stands out as being especially important to you and explain why:

_____

_____

_____

Can you break this goal down into at least 5 smaller steps?

1._____

2._____

3._____

4._____

5._____

What would be an early first step you could take within the next month to move yourself a little bit closer toward this goal?

Facilitator's Instructions for
RELENTLESS DETERMINATION — II

When:

Use this worksheet following the RELENTLESS DETERMINATION - I exercise, page 45, to further explore the concepts, and to steer the discussion, toward goal setting.

Why:

In order to have a semblance of relentless determination one needs to set goals. This worksheet provides a goal setting exercise linked to the very inspiring message of David Rottmayer (see facilitator's instructions for RELENTLESS DETERMINATION - I, page 46). Individuals often neglect to and/or have difficulty breaking goals down into smaller bite-size pieces, so this worksheet includes a place for that.

What:

1. Remind participants about David Rottmayer's message. See page 46.

2. Distribute the worksheets and provide time for participants to complete.

3. Allow for sharing in subgroups or the large group, depending on participants' needs.

4. Facilitate discussion about the process.

5. Finally, have participants buddy up into pairs for further work on their first step (from the last question of the worksheet). Encourage them to supportively inquire about each other's first step over the next few days or weeks. Suggest an appropriate manner for doing this, e.g., they could speak to each other just before or after group time, during the coffee break or through a phone call to each other (the nature and rules of your program / facility may determine this).

Staying Relentlessly Determined!!!

No matter how excited or positive we may feel about a goal we are working toward, external factors will often come up to dampen our enthusiasm. That's life. Do not let it stop you!

Think about some strategies to help yourself stay determined to work toward your goals, no matter what! List your ideas below.

I WILL STAY DETERMINED, NO MATTER WHAT, BY:

_____

_____

_____

_____

_____

_____

_____

_____

_____

_____

_____

_____

_____

_____

Facilitator's Instructions for
STAYING RELENTLESSLY DETERMINED!!!

When: This worksheet is designed to be used after completion of worksheets RELENTLESS DETERMINATION – I, page 45, & II, page 47, to help generate ideas participants will need in order to persevere with their efforts toward goals.

Why: Individuals struggling with illness and / or serious life problems become easily discouraged despite their best efforts to stay on course. They need to be prepared for this dampening of enthusiasm by identifying strategies beforehand. Everyone needs a little help along the way.

What:

1. On the flipchart write the letters of the word DETERMINATION down the left hand side of the flipchart.

2. Ask the group to suggest words or phrases starting with those letters that describe strategies for staying relentlessly determined. Encourage and accept fun or comical ideas as well as serious ones, e.g.,
   D — Don't let the dog eat your homework
   E — Eat a healthy breakfast to start the day off right
   T — Think often about the positive benefits.

3. Distribute worksheets.

4. Instruct participants to record on their worksheets, in their own words, the strategies that apply to themselves, as well as to add any other ideas of their own.

5. Conclude by facilitating discussion about what they have learned from this exercise, as well as the other two exercises on Relentless Determination.

SMALL STEPS FOR DIFFICULT TIMES

*strategies for very difficult days
when very small steps are needed*

Goal Setting:

HOW TO SET GOALS

(WHEN GOAL-SETTING JUST ISN'T YOUR THING!)

If you already set goals for yourself, congratulations!
Some people find it difficult. For some it might sound frightening —
the idea of committing oneself to a goal might feel like too much pressure.
Some are just not in the habit of setting goals, or have never really given it
a chance. Or perhaps the fear of not achieving one's goals can
cause a person to avoid setting goals in the first place.
If goal setting is difficult for you, start small.

DAILY GOALS

Daily goals can be very helpful, and it is a place to start. Try having 2 or 3 goals for the day. Concentrate on those — but if you get more than that accomplished — great!

EXAMPLES:

- Pay a bill . . .
- Call a friend . . .
- Get a haircut . . .
- Have a shower . . .
- Eat some vegetables . . .
- Make a pan of muffins . . .
- Walk around the block . . .
- Read one magazine article . . .
- Practice a relaxation exercise for 10 minutes . . .
- Complete the first page of the income tax form . . .

Make your goals reasonable and realistic *for you*. Be as specific as you can —
try including things like how long, when, with whom, what time and how much.

GET STARTED AND GOOD LUCK!

See Facilitator's Instructions for
GOAL SETTING
on page 56

Goal Setting:

TRY SETTING SOME GOALS

**Don't forget, goals need to be reasonable and realistic for you.
Try to be as specific as you can.**
(e.g. I plan to floss and brush my teeth by noon)
Set either one, two or three goals.

Today I plan to:

1. _____

2. _____

3. _____

To help motivate myself with my goal (or goals), I'll try the following strategy:

If I need encouragement I'll ask for some support or a "pep talk" from:

Once I've completed my goal(s) I look forward to feeling:

I will reward my efforts by:

I will be proud of myself, and so will:

Facilitator's Instructions for
GOAL SETTING: I - HOW TO SET GOALS
II - TRY SETTING SOME GOALS

When:

These two worksheets can be used when participants need instruction and encouragement on using goal setting as a means of getting more organized and motivated with daily tasks.

Why:

Individuals may avoid or neglect goal setting for a number of reasons. They may not know how. They may fear commitment. They may have had unsuccessful past attempts with goal setting and wish to avoid the resulting feelings of failure. Participants with low motivation may be having tremendous difficulty just managing the day. Some instruction on how to set small, reasonable daily goals can be a helpful place to start.

What:

1. Introduce the concept of setting goals by writing the words "GOAL SETTING" on the flipchart, and ask for reactions, good or bad. Ask for a show of hands on how many participants set daily goals. Ask for comments on the difficulty or obstacles of setting daily goals.

2. Distribute worksheet #1, HOW TO SET GOALS, page 53, and ask a volunteer to read aloud. Facilitate discussion about the ideas in the worksheet.

3. Distribute worksheet #2, TRY SETTING SOME GOALS, page 55. Instruct participants to complete it, providing any necessary explanation.

4. Assign participants to subgroups, in which they can share ideas with each other from their completed worksheets.

5. Return to the large group and allow time for discussion on the process of completing the worksheet, as well as the ideas they were able to develop.

6. To conclude, have the words "I can..." written on the flipchart. Request all participants, one by one, to complete the sentence - starter aloud, based on today's session.

WEEKLY ACTIVITIES

Name_____ Date_____

CIRCLE WHAT YOU DID OVER THE PAST WEEK:

household chores   volunteered   walked   read   cooked

baked   helped someone   attended self-help group   phoned a friend

exercised   enjoyed music   class   went bowling

artwork   paid job   watched TV   out to a movie   rented video

went out to_____   sports   family time   went to park   crafts

shopped   socialized with friends   other:_____

NOW, PLACE A STAR BESIDE ANY ACTIVITIES WHICH WERE NEW FOR YOU.

HOW PRODUCTIVE OR ACTIVE DID YOU FEEL DURING THE PAST WEEK?
CIRCLE A NUMBER:

not at all	a little active	somewhat active	quite active	extremely active
1	2	3	4	5

PLAN FOR NEXT WEEK:

_____
(signature)

Facilitator's Instructions for
WEEKLY ACTIVITIES

When: Use this exercise when you want to challenge individuals with low productivity to start thinking about how they spend their time.

Why: Individuals with severe mental illness can fall into a pattern of inactivity that they may or may not recognize. Or they may perceive the activities in which they do partake as having little or no value. This handout is very effective for groups that meet weekly, as it provides a format for group members to regularly share how they have been spending their time. Weekly repetition of the handout produces a subtle reinforcement to increase activity level from week to week.

What:

1. Introduce the concept of tracking weekly activities as a means of exploring productivity.

2. Invite group members to brainstorm the benefits of being active and productive. Flipchart their ideas.

3. Distribute handouts and provide time for participants to complete the first two sections.

4. Divide into pairs and have participants share their written responses with each other.

5. Return to the large group forum and invite them to share how they rated their productivity. Facilitate discussion on how satisfied they are with their level of productivity. Encourage discussion on ideas for getting more active. You may also want to ask them what weekly activities could be added to the first section.

6. Allow time for completion of the last section of the handout, with sharing being optional.

7. Repeat weekly, to promote interest in widening their current range of activity and trying new ideas.

SoMeTHiNG iS BeTTeR THaN NoTHiNG

No matter how small!

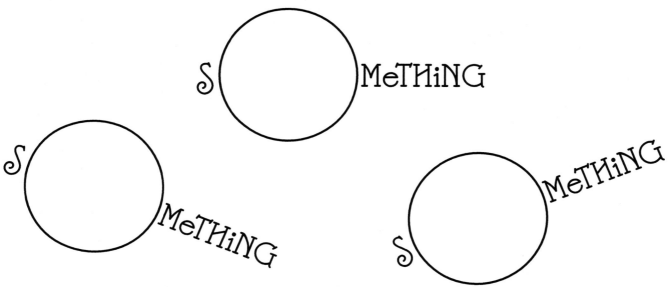

SoMeTHiNG

SoMeTHiNG

SoMeTHiNG

I am only one, but still I am one;
I cannot do everything,
but still I can do something;
And because I cannot do everything,
I will not refuse to do the something
that I can do.

Edward Everett Hale, D.D., LL.D.

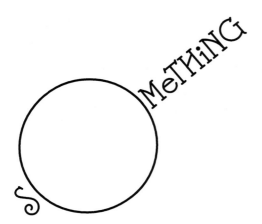

SoMeTHiNG

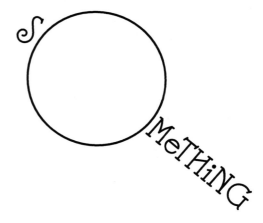

SoMeTHiNG

59

Facilitator's Instructions for
SOMETHING IS BETTER THAN NOTHING

When:
Use this worksheet to inspire a group whose motivation is extremely low and who need to work on very small steps.

Why:
Some individuals become easily overwhelmed by the perceived magnitude of tasks and responsibilities they feel they ought to be doing. The result is often that they then do nothing — and feel even worse, as a result. The prose in the center of the worksheet very simply and succinctly imparts the message that one small step is better than nothing. A momentum often builds for individuals, once one small task or step is accomplished.

What:

1. Ask participants to share a song, poem, book or other piece of written word that has inspired them in the past. Even if they cannot remember exact titles, have them share what they do recall about the piece.

2. Emphasize the power and importance of the written word to human beings and facilitate a brief discussion on this point.

3. Distribute worksheets. Ask for a volunteer to read Edward Hale's poem aloud. Ask for comments and reactions to the piece.

4. Allow time for participants to fill in the "O's" on the worksheet, with either:

   a. a small action they have taken today, or
   b. a small action they will take later in the day.

5. Encourage sharing of all their ideas in the large group.

6. Suggest and provide time in a future group for participants to bring and share their favorite inspiring songs, poems, stories, books, etc.

My "Something is Better than Nothing" Log

date: _____

	PLAN / ACTIVITY	DID IT! (✓)	COMMENTS
morning			
afternoon			
evening			

Facilitator's Instructions for
MY "SOMETHING IS BETTER THAN NOTHING" LOG

When:

Use this worksheet to provide structure for working on small steps and tasks at home.

Why:

Keeping a log at home is a great way to help concretize new concepts and ideas. This log serves to structure participants in their pursuit of trying to accomplish small tasks and responsibilities. It is fairly simple and requires a minimum of writing and time to complete.

What:

1. Ask participants if they have ever journalled or kept a log of any kind. Facilitate discussion about the unique and special impact on us when we put our thoughts in writing ("inking, not just thinking").

2. Distribute worksheet and explain how it is to be used at home to assist with working toward small goals and steps. Use either a hypothetical or real life example to illustrate how to use the form. Ask them what they think of it. Distribute additional copies for home use as needed.

3. Provide time for individuals to record in their logs something they have done so far today. Invite them to share this accomplishment.

4. Organize a future date at which participants will bring completed logs back for further discussion.

I take Inspiration from . . .

Inspiration is necessary to help us feel alive
and keep us moving forward each day.
See if any of these fit for you and please add your own:

A cloudless blue sky

Fresh cut daisies

The Bible

A favorite possession

The sound of birds singing

A cat purring in my lap

A violin solo

A childhood memory

A freshly painted room

A brilliant sunset

A handmade quilt

A thunderstorm

A special photograph

A brisk walk in the woods

AN OLD FAMILY STORY

A child's drawing

The sound of a waterfall

My garden

AN OLD BARN

An inspirational book

Other _____

Other _____

63

Facilitator's Instructions for
I TAKE INSPIRATION FROM ...

When:

Use as a means of exploring the concept of consciously finding inspiration — or use as a quick warm-up to a second worksheet of your choice.

Why:

Individuals struggling with illness, addiction or overwhelming problems in their lives can become very inwardly focused. They may have become quite oblivious to the beauty around them, which ironically could be something they very much need for comfort and motivation. They can benefit from encouragement to become more open to this spiritual practice — to see, hear, smell and be moved by the wonder found in their daily surroundings.

What:

A

1. Introduce the concept of taking inspiration from things around us and facilitate dialogue about the important role of inspiration in recovery.
2. Distribute the worksheet and instruct participants to circle as many items as they wish, as well as adding their own.
3. Sharing at this point can be optional.
4. Invite participants to depict a personal source of inspiration from the worksheet through a creative modality. Provide supplies, time and soft background music for one of the following creative activities:
     - drawing or painting
     - writing a poem or story
     - a collage
5. Provide time for sharing their finished work as well as discussion about their experience of the creative process.
6. Conclude by asking participants to identify a goal for bringing more inspiration into their daily lives.

OR

B

1. To use as a quick warm-up, distribute worksheet and ask participants to circle one or two that apply to themselves and / or to add their own. To add some "sparkle," provide a variety of brightly colored markers.
2. Allow sharing in round robin fashion. Encourage participants to be open to inspiration offered from these sources, on a daily basis.
3. Move on to a second worksheet of your choice.

COPING WITH A REALLY BAD DAY!

 Some questions to ponder:

What have I tried so far to cope?

Have I looked at my list of coping strategies?

Have I tried something new to cope, or am I just trying the same old thing that never seems to work?

Have I reviewed my notes from groups for ideas on coping?

What coping strategies have I used in the past, in a similar situation?

Do I need help from my support system today? For instance:
    Attend a support group
    Talking with a supportive friend or family member on the phone
    Arrange to get together with a supportive person
    Call a care provider or professional for direction
    Call a distress line to talk and get ideas
    Try an internet "chat line" for depressed individuals

Am I trying all the suggestions given to me by others?

Facilitator's Instructions for
COPING WITH A REALLY BAD DAY!

When: Use this worksheet to challenge participants about using everything within their means to help themselves on those really bad days. The worksheet can help to empower individuals at a time when they may be feeling powerless.

Why: Participants dealing with mental illness will most likely run into extremely difficult days to manage. It is just part of the recovery process. Preparing for a crisis is a skill. When an actual crisis is occurring, it is hard to think clearly. They need to learn how to cope with those bad days and to feel they have some control with which to help themselves. Learning to manage bad days will help to avert a more serious crisis from occurring.

What:

1. Introduce the topic and have the group define what constitutes a "really bad day." Flipchart their ideas.

2. Ask for the different coping practices they have tried on those really bad days. Again, flipchart their ideas.

3. Distribute the worksheet. Have it read aloud. Explain its usage — to be used at home as a reference when they are experiencing a really bad day.

4. Spend a bit of time discussing the strategy of having a LIST of coping strategies to refer to at home. Do they all have one? If not, how can they create one. What about group notes and worksheets — how can they be used?

5. Ask participants if the worksheet could or should contain any other helpful questions or suggestions to remind them of effective coping practices to try. Encourage them to jot down these additions on their worksheets, or on the back where there is extra room to write.

··· Managing Today ···

**There are days in recovery when you may be feeling a bit stuck.
Just getting through the day can feel like an enormous struggle.
You may be lacking energy, oomph or hope.
HERE ARE SOME STRATEGIES TO CONSIDER AND TRY.**

- Be gentle with yourself for today. Try to get something accomplished but acknowledge you are not feeling your best.

- Make a list. Be realistic about what you can achieve.

- Prioritize and try pre-planning how to assign your time and schedule for the day.

- You may need to make a decision to concentrate only on the "basics", e.g., bathing, eating, getting dressed, a bit of reading, etc.

- Break things down into smaller steps. Get working on the first step.

- Use a "just do it" approach to steps. Working on one small step at a time helps to builds momentum which helps keep you going.

- A physical activity could really help boost some energy. Consider a short walk that gets you up and moving.

- Use kind and encouraging self-talk. Avoid dwelling on self-criticism and negative thoughts about how you are doing today.

- Appreciate the good stuff that is happening in the moment. Focus on the little things that are positive, e.g., the toast tastes good. Little things can mean a lot!

- Take breaks to practice your slow, deep breathing.

- Reward yourself at times throughout the day, e.g., sit down for a cup of tea and / or watch your favorite TV show.

- Toward the end of the day, write in your journal three things that were positive today.

Facilitator's Instructions for
MANAGING TODAY

When: Use this worksheet when participants are really struggling to just make it through the day, and not able to give much input into producing ideas of their own.

Why: At times group members have a tremendous struggle with low energy and may be experiencing a complete lack of motivation. They may be finding the demands of having to generate ideas in the group too difficult. This worksheet can be used at times like this as it requires a minimum of input from participants.

What:

1. Use a light warm-up to build some interaction between participants, e.g., have them share with a partner a favorite place in their home with a brief explanation. Provide a few minutes for this, and then ask for several examples.

2. Distribute worksheets. Arrange for the worksheet to be read aloud by either one or several participants who are comfortable reading in front of the group. Or use a round robin approach in which participants each read one point from the worksheet.

3. Once it has been read aloud, discuss each point, one by one, elaborating on the points and encouraging participants' comments, questions and other ideas.

4. End by asking participants to identify and share:
   One strategy from the worksheet they are already using.
   One new strategy from the worksheet to try.

REACHING OUT

GETTING OUT

*strategies relating to reaching out to others
and about getting out into the community*

People POWER

Spending large amounts of time alone can lead to feelings of apathy, fatigue and worthlessness. Naturally it is difficult to feel motivated when in this state. Time spent with other people can be a powerful tool to help you gain more energy, interest and *oomph*.

P . . . **P**lan to see someone each and every day.

E . . . **E**nlist a buddy system to get out for walks and other simple activities.

O . . . **O**pportunities to enjoy "people-watching" can be found in many places.

P . . . **P**lay a simple card or board game — it's good for the mind and it relieves you of the pressure of carrying on a conversation if that feels difficult.

L . . . **L**istening to others can help because _____.

E . . . **E**ven a phone conversation is better than nothing.

P . . . **P**ursue people who _____.

O . . . **O**ffer to _____.

W . . . **W**rite letters, send cards and / or use e-mail to keep in touch with people.

E . . . **E**ven short amounts of time with others is helpful — do not feel you have to socialize for hours if that feels too stressful.

R . . . **R**emember that _____.

See Facilitator's Instructions for
PEOPLE POWER
on page 74

People POWER
spending time with others
LOG

date	person / activity	mood brightened	felt more energy	day went smoother	felt "part of" something	motivation improved	no change	comments

Facilitator's Instructions for
PEOPLE POWER
PEOPLE POWER – SPENDING TIME WITH OTHERS LOG

When:

Use these two worksheets for individuals who tend to isolate and avoid spending time with others and social situations.

Why:

Participants may isolate because it feels easier than putting forth the effort to be around others and to use their social skills. However, they then miss out on the magical, special energy that develops as human beings interact and connect with one another. Isolators need to be encouraged to get out, to be with others and to begin to reap the rewards of social contact — even if it feels difficult at first. It does get easier with practice.

What:

1. Introduce this concept by asking participants to share about a recent situation in which they connected in a positive way with another human being.

2. As they share, list on the flipchart some of the words they are using to describe their experiences, e.g., talking, coffee, laughing.

3. Distribute worksheet #1, PEOPLE POWER, page 71. Read the first paragraph aloud and refer to the words listed on the flipchart to illustrate the point that time spent with others is a powerful tool.

4. Read and discuss each idea on the worksheet, and fill in the blanks with their ideas. Emphasize the positive benefits of spending time with others, asking for their input.

5. Invite each participant to state which idea from the worksheet they are willing to try in the next few days.

6. Distribute worksheet #2, PEOPLE POWER – SPENDING TIME WITH OTHERS LOG, page 73. Explain that the "log" is a way to track their progress in spending time with others while acknowledging the positive benefits gained in this pursuit.

7. Encourage participants to work on their logs over a specified time period. Plan to review with individuals at a later date.

WHAT WOULD_____DO?

We all have role models, people who inspire us, who we admire, and from whom we learn. Just thinking about them can give us a lift. A helpful strategy can be to think about how a role model would handle a situation similar to our own, or to imagine the advice or words of wisdom they might offer. This strategy can be a powerful motivator toward taking positive action.

Who might these people be?

— HERE ARE JUST SOME EXAMPLES: —

A respected family member

An individual from group whose approach to life you admire

Someone from your church or temple

A professional helper who is working with you

An influential teacher from the past

A courageous fictional character you have always liked

A figure from history you find inspiring

Someone currently in the media who you admire and respect

A spiritual leader or presence

WHO ARE YOUR ROLE MODELS?

QUESTIONS:

1. Name one of your role models:

_____

2. If he or she were sitting beside you right now, what personal struggle would you want to tell him or her about?

_____

3. What suggestions or words of encouragement do you think he or she might offer you?

_____

Facilitator's Instructions for
WHAT WOULD_____DO?

When:	This worksheet introduces a strategy in which group members visualize the actions or suggestions a role model would make. This can be helpful since participants do not always have an opportunity to directly speak to an individual who could assist them in their lives.

Why:	As social creatures, we interact with others, observe others, and learn important lessons from others. Group members can learn valuable lessons from role models in their lives, ranging from people they personally know, to people from the history books or famous media stars. Reflecting on how other people manage life problems can be illuminating. Also, learning to say to themselves the words of encouragement that they imagine a role model might say, can be a powerful motivational strategy.

What:

1. Introduce the concept of role models by asking participants to create a list of people they admire on the flipchart. Encourage them to even think of cartoon characters, e.g., Lisa Simpson.

2. Ask for a few examples from participants of a recent situation in which a role model inspired them to take positive action.

3. Distribute worksheets. Facilitate discussion about how role models can impact our lives.

4. Subdivide into small groups and ask participants to review the list of examples on the worksheet and to share who are their role models.

5. Provide time for participants to individually work on the questions at the bottom of the worksheet.

6. Facilitate discussion of participants' findings from working through the three questions. Encourage sharing of their answers and their thoughts about implementing this strategy in the upcoming days and weeks.

The Buddy System

The Buddy System means two (sometimes more) people, who agree to help motivate each other with a shared or similar goal.

Do you have a buddy?

EXAMPLES:

- Attend a new activity together for the first time
- Make a morning wake-up call to encourage getting out of bed
- Exercise or walk together
- Meet for coffee or tea to get out of the house
- Other examples could be: _____

TIPS:

When asking someone to buddy with you, be clear about the goal you are working on. Agree on the type of support you both need, what you are both willing to do and not do.

Get started.

Celebrate your progress.

Occasionally review how the buddy plan is working.

Other tips: _____

_____

QUESTIONS TO CONSIDER:

1. What goal are you working on which could benefit from a buddy system?

_____

2. Who could you possibly ask?

_____

3. How could you support each other?

_____

4. What is a first step you could take in setting up a buddy system?

_____

Facilitator's Instructions for
THE BUDDY SYSTEM

When:

Teach this strategy when group members are working on goals in which a buddy could be an appropriate and helpful resource.

Why:

Mutual support can be tremendously effective for people whose motivation is low. Some goals (like exercise) can be very difficult to work on alone. Depending on the nature of your group members, it might be advisable to include some caution about healthy versus unhealthy dependence on a buddy. You might want to give some specific examples of inappropriate reliance on a buddy, e.g., calling a buddy for crisis support that is clearly beyond the scope of the buddy.

What:

1. Write the term "buddy system" on the flipchart. Ask the group for their initial impressions of this idea, and flipchart their responses.

2. Ask for examples of the buddy system that participants are currently engaged in. Facilitate discussion about the benefits of buddying.

3. Distribute the worksheet. Read aloud and discuss the "Examples" and "Tips" sections. Provide discussion about inappropriate / unhealthy use of a buddy, should this be a potential problem for your group members.

4. Provide time for individuals to quietly complete the "Question" portion of the worksheet.

5. Encourage sharing of participants' first steps in setting up a buddy system for themselves.

6. In a future group, provide time to review how participants' buddy systems are working.

Going Somewhere NEW

I WANT TO GO TO:

1. I haven't gone there before because:

_____

2. Some of my fears about going there now are:

_____

3. I think it would be good for me to go there because:

_____

4. Strategies I can use to get myself there:

_____

5. Supports I can use to get myself there:

_____

_____

I COMMIT TO . . .

_____
SIGNATURE

Facilitator's Instructions for
GOING SOMEWHERE NEW

When:

Use this worksheet to help group members develop a plan for trying something new in the community.

Why:

Getting out and trying something new in the community may be difficult for some people. Because of illness or other struggles, they may have been isolated at home for a period of time and may have lost their confidence about being part of a community. Their comfort zone may include only a few community resources. They may have a high level of anxiety about trying new things or they may feel unmotivated and apathetic about the world around them. This exercise stimulates some interest and ideas about trying a new event or activity in the community.

What:

1. Introduce the topic by asking participants to share the last time they went somewhere in the community for the first time. How did it feel?

2. Ask participants to identify a small goal of trying something new in their community. Remind them, there is no commitment at this point — just a willingness to start to develop a plan. Write goals on flipchart (optional).

3. Distribute worksheets and ask participants to write their stated goal in the first box. Explain that the following five questions will help them explore possible barriers as well as motivational strategies to assist with pursuing this goal. At this point discourage completing the last box.

4. Invite participants to share their answers with each other. Ask if they see some common themes in the answers. Generate discussion on their feelings about committing themselves to their goals, and the idea of setting a date by which their goal will be completed.

5. Invite participants to fill in the bottom box, stating the commitment and signing their name. This step needs to be optional. How does it feel?

6. Close by asking for feedback regarding how the completion of this worksheet has helped with motivation to venture out to a new activity in the community.

Let's Go On An OUTING!

TO. . . _____

Briefly describe the outing:

_____

_____

_____

Location: _____

_____

Estimated cost: _____

_____

Travel Requirements: _____

_____

BENEFITS OF ATTENDING:

1. _____

_____

2. _____

_____

3. _____

_____

Facilitator's Instructions for
LET'S GO ON AN OUTING

When: Use this worksheet as a means of involving group members in the planning of a group outing.

Why: Individuals with mental health challenges can greatly benefit from program outings. Outings offer a safe and supportive environment for group members to practice skills and work through fears and anxieties. Among other things, outings can help to:
- break a pattern of isolation
- improve skill and confidence in taking public transportation
- motivate individuals to seek out new community experiences

What: A trip to the mall, a nearby park, the bowling alley, an art gallery, out for lunch or a coffee shop are all examples of outings that can be highly successful.

1. As an ice-breaker, start with a round robin by asking participants to complete, "My favorite place to go is . . ."

2. Introduce the idea of a group outing, chosen and planned by the participants themselves. Explain that subgroups will each make a rough plan for an outing of their choosing, which will then be presented to the whole group for a vote. Point out any limitations they will have to consider, e.g., time frame, travel distance, etc.

3. Divide into subgroups of 3 or 4 and provide worksheets. Allow approximately 15 - 20 minutes for this step.

4. Upon completion of the worksheets, have each subgroup present their idea to the large group. Allow for questions and answers, but discourage judging or criticizing. Facilitate a playful approach to the voting.

5. Take a vote on the different outing ideas.

6. A small planning committee of participants may then be formed to continue with the organization of the outing.

Please join us for an OUTING!

Facilitator's Instructions for
PLEASE JOIN US FOR AN OUTING!

When: Once the group has finalized plans for their outing (see worksheet LET'S GO ON AN OUTING, page 81), enhance their level of motivation for the activity by involving them in the creation of posters.

Why: Individuals experiencing low motivation may find it difficult to feel interested in committing to a planned group outing. Any preparatory activities that they can take part in, will serve to heighten their sense of being part of it and involved. The act of making posters to advertise the event can provide a relaxed opportunity to feel a sense of ownership and direct creativity toward a specific and useful result. The posters can then be displayed to inform and remind participants about the upcoming outing.

What:

1. Make available various art materials such as colored markers, pencils, rulers, paint, brushes, magazines, scissors, etc.

2. Offer participants a choice of working independently or in subgroups to create a poster, to advertise details of the outing. Encourage creativity.

3. Provide necessary time for participants to create their works of art.

4. Once completed, invite participants to walk around room and view the completed posters.

5. Have participants hang their posters in strategic locations around the room, department or building.

6. If hanging posters is not permitted, an equally effective exercise would be to create flyers which participants could trade with each other to take home.

Outcome of our GROUP OUTING

BEFORE I WENT ON THE OUTING I FELT: _____

AFTER I WENT ON THE OUTING I FELT: _____

RATE YOURSELF ON HOW SUCCESSFUL THE OUTING WAS FOR YOU:

CIRCLE ONE:

not at all successful	a little successful	somewhat successful	quite successful	extremely successful
1	2	3	4	5

THE BENEFITS FOR ME IN ATTENDING THE OUTING WERE:

☐ It got me out of the house

☐ I learned about a new place or activity in the community

☐ I was able to laugh

☐ I practiced my social skills

☐ I gained confidence in taking the bus or subway

☐ I developed a new interest

☐ I felt proud of myself

☐ I relaxed

☐ I feel more comfortable with my social skills

☐ I feel more motivated to try new things in the community

☐ I feel more motivated in general

☐ Other: _____

Facilitator's Instructions for
OUTCOME OF OUR GROUP OUTING

When: Use this worksheet following the group outing (see worksheet titled LET'S GO ON AN OUTING!, page 81) to help participants observe the benefits they experienced from attending such an event. In addition, the worksheet can introduce or reinforce the concept of negative anticipation and how this negativity impacts on motivation.

Why: Participants at the outing undoubtedly had a positive experience. It will be helpful, however, to reflect on, and discuss within the group setting, the benefits that occurred. Some individuals have a longstanding habit of focusing more on the negative than the positive, and this discussion can help them to recognize and break out of this ineffective pattern.

What:

1. Introduce this concept by starting with a round robin, in which participants are asked to identify their favorite part of the outing.

2. Distribute the worksheets and ask participants to verbally share their answers to the first two questions with a partner.

3. Discuss the phenomenon of negatively anticipating upcoming events. Do participants think they engaged in this cognitive distortion, based on how they answered the first two questions?

4. Provide time for participants to independently complete the remainder of the worksheet. Ask them to place a star beside one or two of the benefits most important to them.

5. Divide into subgroups of 3 or 4 and encourage sharing of the rating scale and benefits. Ask the subgroups to discuss any ideas from today's exercise that can help to increase motivation in the future.

6. Return to large group and process new learning from today's exercise and discussion. As a final point to consider, ask the question: What is a new community activity or event you will each seriously consider trying?